Edition Schott

Nikolai Kapustin

Николай Капустин

* 1937

T0070964

Sonata No. 9

(1995)

for Piano
für Klavier
для фортепиано

opus 78

Authorized Edition

ED 23151
ISMN 979-0-001-20781-2

www.schott-music.com

SCHOTT

Mainz · London · Madrid · Paris · New York · Tokyo · Beijing
© 2019 Schott Music GmbH & Co. KG, Mainz · Printed in Germany

Sonata No. 9
opus 78

I

Nikolai Kapustin
*1937

Allegro ($\quarternote$ = 132)

4

6

II

Larghetto (♩ = 60)

Interludio

III

Allegro ma non troppo ($\mathord{\downarrow} = 120$)

36